MONKEY IN A LION'S SKIN

Story by Paul White, illustrations by Peter Oram

This adventure of Toto the monkey and his jungle friends comes from Jungle Doctor's Monkey Tales *published by The Paternoster Press Ltd., Exeter.*

ISBN 0 85364 158 7

Copyright © 1973 The Paternoster Press Ltd.

First published 1973

Made and printed in Great Britain for The Paternoster Press Ltd., 3 Mount Radford Crescent, Exeter, Devon, by Purnell & Sons Ltd., Paulton (Somerset) and London

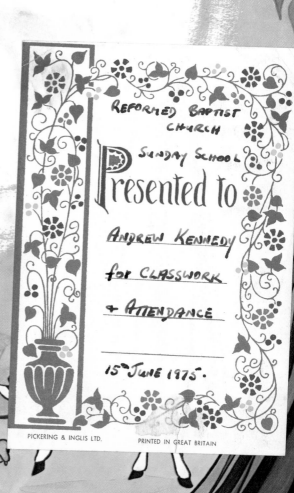

Everyone, except Boohoo the hippo, thought it was a lovely day in the jungle. Boohoo had a question that went round and round in his head.

"Um, Twiga," he said to giraffe, "do lions climb trees?"

"They do sometimes," said Twiga.

"Ooh, good," nodded hippo. "Look at that one. He was swinging by his – um – tail a minute ago. Um, do you think he's ferocious?"

"I think we're safe," smiled Twiga. "Let's say good morning."

"Hallo up there," called hippo.

"Eh? Oh, Roar! Don't you come any closer or I'll leap from this branch and tear you both to pieces."

"You will, eh!" said Twiga. "And who are you?"

"Can't you see? I'm the King of Beasts."

"Toto, it's only monkey wisdom to run round in a moth-eaten lion's skin and say you're a lion."

"Don't talk to me like that, giraffe, or I'll eat you. I'm not a monkey any more. I've become a lion. I do what lions do. I eat what lions eat. I say what lions say – Roar! And I go where lions go."

Twiga spoke gently.

"You can't become a lion by imitating lions."

"Oh?" mumbled Boohoo.

"Oh no?" shouted Toto. "This lion skin fits perfectly.
I'm noble and fierce and . . ."

"To become a lion," went on Twiga, "you would have to be
born all over again and become a new creature."

But Toto was taking no notice. He strode along snarling. "Watch my lion-like steps, Boohoo," he roared. "Aren't I clever? I wonder how many smart animals there are in the jungle."

"There's one less than you think," said Twiga. "You could be playing a very dangerous game."

Hippo nodded slowly. "If you — um — meet other animals, what will happen then?"

Toto chortled, "I met hyaena this morning. He took one look at me and bolted. He knows a lion when he sees one."

"But what happens," asked Twiga, "if you meet a bad-tempered rhino or a hungry leopard?"

Toto made growling noises. "What will they see?
Me, the King of the Jungle. When they hear me growl
they'll tremble. When they hear me roar, they'll run."

"Um," thought Boohoo, "perhaps the best way to teach a monkey something is to let him find out for himself." His nose suddenly sent him a warning.

"Oops, look out, everyone. Leopard is coming.

Quick, Toto, up into a tree before he sees you.

Come on, Twiga."

"Do what Boohoo says," called Twiga. "You can play lions later."

But Toto sniffed. "I'm not frightened even if you are.

Leopard knows what to expect from lions. ROAR !

Bye-bye, Boohoo. Hide if you're scared."

"So leopard's coming, is he?

I'll let him know who's here. ROAR — ROAR."

He shook his mane and grinned.

"That should send a shiver up his spine."

Leopard growled.

"Who did that?" demanded Toto.

Leopard growled again.

"Run, monkey!" shouted Twiga.

"Run fast!" bellowed Boohoo.

Toto turned and looked at leopard.

The leopard growled deep in his throat.

Toto's voice suddenly became squeaky. "Stay where you are.

Nice pussy. Stand back. Stand back, I say. Am I

the King of Beasts or . . . HELP!"

The lion's skin fell off

Toto rushed up a tree and far out on a limb.

Leopard sat waiting and watching.

He waited all day, thinking all the time of monkey for dinner.

Leopard was still waiting when the sun set and the
moon rose, and then, while he had a very small snooze,
Twiga ran underneath the tree and Toto escaped by
the skin of his teeth.

As giraffe galloped away, Toto said, "You saved me;
thank you, Twiga."

Then in a small voice, "I was wrong, and you don't become a
lion by doing things or saying things or wearing things."

"That was only monkey wisdom," agreed Twiga.

Do you think Toto understands now?